RHYME AND RE...

These poems you'll find are a
Illustrations and messages n
A book that's unique
So why not take a peek?
It's a world both inspiring and humorous.

It's primarily written for children,
But so many boxes it ticks.
You can read to each other,
As it says on the cover,
Whether 6 or 106.

*'A glorious collection of witty, educational, fun poems with a message,
whatever your age.'
JL, School teacher*

*'A fun book of poems with brilliantly quirky illustrations, to be enjoyed by adults
and children alike.'
BM, book reviewer and author*

*Amazing, fantastic and brilliant - will make you laugh your socks off!
Charlie, aged 10*

**Copyright words and illustrations
© Judy Wolfson-Davies 2020**

www.custardontoast.com

Second Edition September 2020
First self-published in hardback in May 2020.

CONTENTS

ABOUT THE AUTHOR

Judy Wolfson-Davies was born in Cardiff. On leaving high school she taught at primary level for a year, before going abroad on an International Youth Leaders course. Having qualified as a Youth Leader at Westhill Training College (Birmingham University), obtaining a Distinction, she was then employed as a full time leader of a London youth club.

Judy was also the Director of XUK Children's Holiday Activities, Adlib Drama Workshop, a Children's Party Agency and Poolside Manor Swimming School in North London (which she and her husband designed and built). She was a founder member of the British Activity Holiday Association, was an 'Adult and Youth' magistrate for ten years and is a member of Equity. She still teaches First Aid in schools to teachers and children.

During much of this substantial career of working with children, Judy has also been a semi-professional lyricist/playwright and has written and produced musicals for TV, theatre, charities and youth organisations.

Judy is married with two children and two grandchildren.

ACKNOWLEDGEMENTS

Sophie Aurélia Young for her superb and imaginative illustrations; my husband Ivor, my family and grandchildren for their patience, technical help and constructive comments.

JW-D September 2020

CUSTARD ON TOAST

When Great Aunt Hilda visits me
She always loves to cook.
They are the weirdest recipes
In Great Aunt Hilda's book.

She says, "I'll make a special meal
Because you are my hero!"
I wish Aunt Hilda would get real;
Her cooking skills are zero!

"For you I'll cook your favourite food;
It's not a Sunday Roast.
It won't be boiled, it won't be stewed;
Ta-da! **Custard On Toast**!"

"But Great Aunt Hilda that's not nice,
Toast with yucky custard."
"Then add some sugar, add some spice,
Some ketchup and some mustard.

And when you've eaten, we'll go out,
I'll challenge you at conkers."
Aunt Hilda is without a doubt
The best, but truly bonkers!

SPELLBOUND

CHOKLAT

This poem needs a spell check,
You may find some mistakes.
Detectives, **you** identify
The real words from the fakes.

So let's inspect the crime seen
For clues, before deciding
What line to take, so we can find
Exactly where their hiding.

Scool

Jiraf

Five offending words in print,
Not wanting to be found;
And more, if you extend your search,
You need to check around.

A star for every one you find,
As long as you correct it.
A Sheriff's badge for all of them,
If your a good detective.

aminals

Eleven guilty words, so when
The culprits have confest,
Round them up and reed their rights,
And then make your arrest!

GOOD IN-TENTS

"Off you go, enjoy yourselves," exclaimed my smiling Mum.
I didn't think to ask her why she didn't want to come.
The three of us went camping, my Dad and us two boys;
I couldn't get to sleep all night 'cos there was so much noise.

My Father snored and Billie sneezed and then went to the loo.
The best way to describe it was like sleeping in a zoo.
My Mother's choice was very wise, our soggy socks all smell.
The bugs and rain, it's not her thing, she stayed in a hotel.
So would I go again? Oh yes! Love beans on toasted bread,
But if it's freezing cold and wet, I'll send my Mum instead!

 # ODD SOCKS

My brother, me and Papa,
We love to wear odd socks.
We make sure that they're all mixed up
Inside the odd sock box!

Six socks we have for playing,
For working and for best.
Striped ones, patterned, red or blue,
Each different from the rest.

Saves time for Mum and Grandma,
From finding matching pairs.
We say, "We've come from Planet Mars,"
To anyone who stares.

Cos clothes are just for wearing,
Grow into them, then out.
Coordinated colours,
Who knows what that's about?

Some mornings when I'm rushing,
For my underwear I hunt,
My pants will end up inside out
And sometimes back to front.

We all get dressed the way we like;
Mum says that we can choose.
So why does she get frazzled
When we go out in odd shoes?

PAWS FOR THOUGHT

Annabelle had lots of pets, she loved them very much.
A kitten and a goldfish, a rabbit in a hutch.
A puppy who was 6 months old, she'd take it for a walk.
A hamster and a gerbil and a parrot that would squawk.

It took a lot of work to keep them happy every day;
Brushing, wiping out the cage, whilst friends went out to play.
One day 'out of the blue' she said, "I'm bored with all this stuff,
Cleaning, feeding, walking them, I've really had enough.

I'm going out to play **right now**," and out the door she hurried.
The pets had quite a shock, they were upset and very worried.
The puppy called a meeting, "Now listen every one,
I have a good idea," he woofed, "this is what should be done.
We'll write a list for Annabelle to help her plan her day,
School and homework, housework, pet time; **then** go out to play!"

She crept back home and saw the list, and thought that's very weird.
Who's written this? She wondered (all her pets had disappeared!).
The animals have run away, it must be them I guess.
"Come back," she cried, "I didn't mean to leave you in a mess;"
And one by one they scampered back, showing their affection,
But said, "Your love is not enough; we need care and protection."

"I promise from now on, dear pets, to keep you safe and well.
I'll brush and walk you, clean the poo, each day," said Annabelle.
I didn't put you first and so I'm sorry, that was wrong.
The dog said "Woof," the cat "Meow," and parrot sang a song!

MINDING THEIR OWN BUZZINESS

Bees are buzzy, Bees are busy,
Big Bees buzzing, make you dizzy,
Bees can stingy, with their thingy,

Bee called Bridgette, makes you fidget,
Bee called Betty, loves spaghetti,
Bee called Biddy, makes you giddy.

Bee collector, making nectar,
Only females, on their Bee tails,
Bees in flowers, happy hours.

Bees at home with honeycomb,
Making honey, sweet and runny.
Bees will make it, humans take it.

You can taste it, mustn't waste it,
Smooth or sticky on your bicky,
Good to try some, let's go buy some!

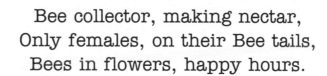

UP THE DOWNSTAIRS DOODAH

In the near off land of Thingymajig
Where Wotsits are in charge,
While fast asleep at Ding Dong hour
The Doodah is at large.

Up the downstairs he's been seen
In gum boots and bow tie.
It's said by some and others too,
He lives on Thingy Pie.

You'll know him by his Whatsitcalled,
It's polka-dotted pink.
His Goodle watch will just strike three,
Or green striped four I think.

He lost his Oojah more or less,
He tried to make it stay.
He searched for years, without success,
Then found it straight away!

His body is as long as this,
Or may be long as that.
He's very thin but eats too much,
So now he's very fat.

And in a minute much too soon,
He'll tell you later how.
But please don't ask him, can't you see?
He's very busy now.

So next time, or the time before,
Remember, ask him why?
And he will tell you in return,
For just one Thingy Pie!

A SPIDER'S YARN

Why do I take fright
When a spider's in sight?
I can't even jump on a chair.
Whilst stuck to the spot,
At that little black dot,
I stand like a statue and stare.

Perhaps one so hairy
Is bound to be scary,
And yet I'm MUCH bigger than he.
And how does he view it?
If only I knew it.
I'll ask "Are you frightened of me?"

"Little girl, I'm so busy,
My webs leave me dizzy,
A stroll I enjoy day or nightly.
I meet many people
As tall as a steeple;
They all treat me most impolitely.

I never would harm them
And yet I alarm them,
You're the first that I've ever befriended.
I cannot claim beauty,
But I do my duty,
Catch flies with my silk webs, quite splendid.

So listen please do,
I'm not handsome, it's true,
And I frightened Miss Muffet away.
But tell her this spider
That sat down beside her,
Just wanted to ask 'Will you play?'"

BYE BYE BUN

My rabbit 'Bun' he died today;
We'll bury him tonight.
I'll miss him now he's gone away,
So I will do what's right.

I'll say, "Goodbye, we did have fun,
And though you're in the ground,
I know in Bunny Heaven,
You'll still be bobbing round."

We'll say a special prayer for Bun
That everybody knows.
"Our Heavenly Father and the Son,
And *in the hole 'e goes!* "

MY OWN POEM

NAME AND AGE

PETE THE TWEET

A perky young parrot called Pete,
Always had some new gossip to tweet.
He would hear people speak, with their human-like beak,
Every word that he heard, would repeat.
Every word that he heard, would repeat.

"Humans are strange," said Pete Parrot,
"Their feathers are grey, blonde and carrot.
If you mimic their voice, they clap and rejoice,
As if you are Callas or Garrett."
As if you are Callas or Garrett.

"Such behaviour is wholly absurd.
Fancy making us copy each word.
If parrots should talk, then humans should squawk,
And who would know human from bird?"
And who would know human from bird?

Talking parrots, it seems are the rage,
And so, as I'm perched in my cage,
If I say something rude, they increase my food,
The ruder, the higher the wage!
The ruder, the higher the wage!

WHAT AM I?

Now you see me, now you don't,
It's not my scene to hang about.
Will you catch me? No, you won't.
As fast as light, I'm in and out.

I just flew in from Nanjypoo,
That's where I left my family.
And if you ask me what they do,
It's very much the same as me.

I am invisible you see,
So no-one knows when I'm around.
You might ask, what's the point of me?
Now there's an answer to be found!

And when you've found it in your mind,
Take pen and paper, you can draw me,
From the front and from behind;
And make believe you really saw me!

There are no clues to who I am,
Except what I devour the most.
Could be chicken, could be jam,
Could be Custard - could be Toast!

DRAW A PICTURE BELOW OF WHAT YOU THINK I AM

STUFF

I'm filling my pockets with all sorts of stuff,
Elastic bands, marbles, there's never enough;
And always a space as my pockets are deep.
I check them each night before going to sleep.

I'm collecting the things that one day I might need,
A conker, a chain, a key-ring, a bead.
I add to my pockets which never get full,
Bottle tops, wire, sticky tape, cotton-wool.

One evening when I was on pocket patrol,
My fears were confirmed, I discovered a hole!
That's why there was space, I just couldn't win,
More stuff falling out, than stuff going in!

Can't play hide and seek, too easy to find me!
You'd follow the stuff that was trailing behind me.
I'm no good at sewing, the holes I can't mend,
So filling my pockets has come to an end.

But a new collection of pebbles and rocks,
I have started to make in a big wooden box.
It's a very strong box, a box I can trust.
It will last me forever; no holes and no rust.

So sturdy, it's made to hold boulders and granite,
And the best rock collection on all of the planet!
I'll keep on collecting all kinds of new stuff,
Even with a full box; there's never enough!

DRAW SOME OF THE THINGS THAT YOU COLLECT

HOW LUCKY AM I?

How lucky am I to have a best friend
Who shares all her books and her toys?
How lucky am I to have a best friend
Out of all of the girls and the boys?

And though we may differ in so many ways,
(She has an unusual name!)
Our colour, our clothes, are from different worlds,
Yet somehow we're so much the same!

We play lots of games and giggle a lot,
And together we both walk to school.
We hug each other and try not to cry,
If at times other children are cruel.

But it doesn't matter, whatever they say,
Each other we always defend.
How sad for them, but how lucky am I,
That she is my very best friend.

WALLY WITH A BROLLY

I met a young fella who had an umbrella
Open, when sunny and bright.
I met him again, it was pouring with rain,
It was closed; I thought, something's not right!

He said, "When it's wetter, I like it much better,
I have little use for a brolly.
If I want to keep dry, I just wear a bow tie."
I think he is right off his trolley!

"But a great substitute, when I've no parachute,
And I'm planning to jump from a plane."
Though the jury is out, I wasn't in doubt,
And my verdict? This fella's insane!

BEST AT LAST

"It's 7 o'clock, oh my poor head"
(Tim wished that he could stay in bed).
"It's sports day UGH! I wouldn't mind,
But I am always left behind.
I wouldn't care, not being fast,
But must I always come in last?

Oh well, that is the way it goes,
I'll try again, one never knows.
If it were only me to run,
I'd come in first, that would be fun.
I'll do my best, I can't do more,
Try even harder than before."

Time for school, so off Tim went
With many doubts, but good intent.
Whilst unbeknown to him a plan,
Was being hatched:
THE MATCHSTICK MAN!

Who's always there to lend a hand.
A very clever scheme he'd planned.
Tim was never good at sport,
So he would give him his support.

Now MATCHSTICK MEN are super creatures,
Having extra special features.
They're skinny, versatile and bold,
Never growing up, or old!

They're full of mischief, full of fun,
And do their best for everyone.
And knowing Tim was very tense,
He would boost his confidence.

Spectators cheered with all their heart,
At all the children taking part.
Tho' Mum and Dad gave him a wave,
Poor Timmy didn't feel too brave.

He looked round at all the crowd,
Oh how he'd love to make them proud.
Egg and spoon, and running races,
Puffing, panting, red hot faces.

Across the track a banner hung.
The words were clear to old and young.

'Do your best, that is the aim.
What matters how you play the game.
Run your socks off, don't give in,
Good luck and may the best man win.'

The MATCHSTICK MAN had seen it too,
And knew exactly what to do.
The time had come for Tim to race;
The whistle blew, with rapid pace
The children sprinted out of sight.
The MATCHSTICK MAN said, "Strike a light!"

The little lad he had in mind,
Was struggling on, and way behind.
The sign blew gently in the breeze.
The MATCHSTICK MAN leapt up with ease.
Some letters he would re-arrange,
The meaning of the sign would change.

Tim came in last, but what a show,
Like MATCHSTICK MAN, his cheeks aglow.
Across the line he made a dive,
And gave the MATCHSTICK MAN 'high-five'.
"I really tried my best," said Tim,
Then saw the banner, just for him!

**'Best at last, that's where you came.
What mattered how you played the game.
You ran your socks off, job well done,
You are a MATCH for anyone!'**

PARTY ANIMALS

Jim jolly giant Jellyfant,
Goes galloping and gobble.
Part picking plums, part potting plants,
With one wet wibble wobble.

The manky mauve Meringue-Utang,
Comes crawly crunch and crispy.
His hair all hippy hoppy hangs,
With whiskers, wild and wispy.

The prickly pimpled Porkypie,
New needles nip and nasty,
Can crunch or crackle, cripple, cry,
A plump and pickled pastie.

But bouncing barefoot, bobbing bum,
Comes criss-cross Currant Bunny.
Two tumble turns, tail over tum,
Slips sloppy side up sunny.

For fatty Flippopotoftea,
For Fumble Bumble Beastie,
For fangs, for flippers, fly or flea,
For all, *THE FOREST FEASTIE!*

A WIGGLE AND A GIGGLE

The Lion gave a mighty roar, "Remember I am King."
The Jungle Folk queued by the door, each one would 'do his thing.'
Upon his bed the Lion lay, he'd been there quite a while,
'Though strong as iron' some did say, he could not raise a smile.
And all the Jungle Folk would try and change this situation,
A dance, a song, a silly joke, to end the Lion's frustration.

First by beating on his chest, the Cheeky Chimp began,
Jumping up and down with zest; the King remained dead pan!
Next was Jimmy the Giraffe, he'd give the King a ride.
Surely that would make him laugh, his neck could be a slide.
"Jimmy you're too tall for me," the stubborn Lion said,
"And riding you, I'm bound to fall, I'd rather stay in bed."

Then came along a big beaked bird, by name of Toofy Toucan.
He said, "King when I say the word, just laugh, yes, me and you can."
The King said, "Thanks but it's a no, I'd rather take a rest."
He told the Toucan he should go; he wasn't much impressed.

"I will make you laugh out loud," said Meany the Hyena,
"I am the expert in this crowd" (you really should have seen her).
She showed her rotten teeth and grinned, then pulled a silly face.
She blew her nose and let off wind, a terrible disgrace.
"D'you think that my performance rocked? Perhaps a little tweak?"
The Jungle Folk were all so shocked, that none of them could speak!

Now all the animals were there, the Panther and the Monkey,
The Hippy Hippo, Dancing Bear all fighting fit and funky.
They couldn't make, not one of them, their Lion laugh at all,
Until one day into the den crawled something very small.

It was the creepy Centipede, his legs were never ending,
"To make you laugh I can succeed, and that's what I'm intending."
But they all sneered, "Make him laugh? You ugly little thing."
"Go home," said Jim the tall Giraffe, "do not insult our King."

The Lion said, "HEY! wait a minute, give the guy a chance,
Perhaps there might be something in it, do you sing or dance?"
"Oh no," replied the Centipede, "I simply have the knack,
So now if we are both agreed, please roll on to your back."

And so the little leggy bug climbed on the Lion's belly,
Soon he began to jitterbug, and wobble like a jelly!
A hundred little hairy feet, you should have seen him wiggle.
Said Lion, "I admit defeat," as he began to giggle.

The Centipede crawled round and round, the Lion shrieked with laughter.
The den filled with the sound of joy and so it was thereafter.
"You saved me in my hour of need, by being so persistent,
I'll make you, Mr Centipede, my personal assistant."

So, here's a lesson for you all, don't be so disbelieving.
They said too ugly and too small, but looks can be deceiving.
"From my bed you made me budge, you helped me to recover.
From now on I will never judge *a bug just by its cover*."

MONKEY BUSINESS

Said Monkey to the Acorn, "You are a tiny bloke."
"So what," replied the Acorn, "One day I'll be an oak."
"Oh yeah, yeah," scoffed the Monkey, "And I'll be a Gorilla."
Said Acorn, "You'll need stuffing with a ton of Polyfilla!
But me, I'll be enormous, I'll grow the tallest trunk."
"And **I** will be the Great King Kong, the famous Mighty Hunk."
Alas it seemed that neither, would win this silly race.
Monkey slipped and squashed Acorn, then fell flat on his face.
Respect for one another's roles, without the need to boast,
Would have made them 'Champions' in this book,
'CUSTARD ON TOAST'!

SHAKE RATTLE AND ROLL

If cuckoos are cuckoo and Mad Hatters mad ,
Walnuts are nutters, and ladder's a lad,
Fathers are fat and granddads are grand ,
Magpies are pies and a sandwich is sand.
Rockwell will rock and Shakespeare will shake,
Rowling will roll and a rattle will snake,
Robin will rob and Friar Tuck fry,
Snoopy will snoop and a spider will spy.
This riddle is riddled, so what's your reply?
If you know the answer, the question is why?

A RUBBISH POEM

It's easy to figure, if we hired a digger
And people would all do their bit;
We wouldn't be faced
With litter and waste;
We'd chuck the whole lot in a pit.

"No way," said Amanda, with outspoken candour,
"Good thinking, but not good enough.
We'll find a solution
To end this pollution,
Some way we'll get rid of that stuff."

"The parks are so dirty," said Ali and Bertie,
"We must get together and act.
The bins are all busting
The smell is disgusting,
It's time that this issue was cracked."

"The problem," said Daisy, "is people are lazy,
They won't walk three steps to a bin."
"You're right," said young Poppet,
"They throw it or drop it,
So how can we possibly win?"

"Revolting," said Nelly, "disgusting and smelly,
Litterbugs, all of you stink!"
"The answer," said Michael,
"Is we should recycle,
Let's ask everyone what they think!"

So, Mika and Molly, and Charlie and Oli,
And children all over the land,
What are your ideas
From you and your peers?
It's time that you all made a stand!

A SPOT OF BOTHER

One day I woke up very hot, all splotchy, blotchy, patchy.
My body covered all in spots, so itchy, scritchy, scratchy.
I was so spotty everywhere, my head down to my socks,
On my back and in my hair; I'd got the chicken pox!

I couldn't go to school; OK, because I was contagious.
But staying in the house all day? I thought that was OUTRAGEOUS!
But hurray, two weeks on, those nasty spots have cleared.
No more calamine, they've gone! They simply disappeared!

Now little brother's got the bug, I know just how he feels,
And so I gave him one big hug and told him it soon heals.
Poor thing, he's covered head to toe, his tummy and his botty.
It won't be long before they go, it's awful, being spotty.

And all our friends came round to play, so they could catch it too.
"Very strange," I hear you say, "What a thing to do."
But no, it isn't strange at all, our mummies have been told,
It's bad enough when you are small, but horrid when you're old!

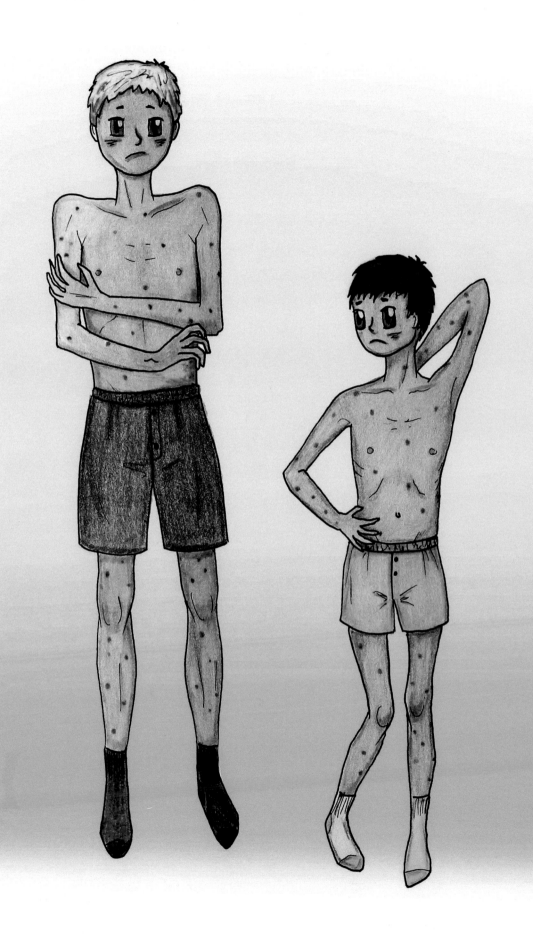

HEADS AND TOES

There once was a young man from Poole,
Who refused to get ready for school.
His father said, "Son,
This just isn't done,
For you to be playing the fool.

The pupils are already there;
For your lessons you have to prepare.
I'll write you a note,
Now go get your coat,
Brush your teeth please and tidy your hair."

"But Dad, I just don't want to go,
I've a very big cut on my toe.
It's really no use
I've got my excuse;
If I stay at home no-one will know!"

"Not true, all you need is a plaster,
It's hardly a major disaster.
Do you want a detention
And lose all your pension?
After all, Son, you are the Headmaster!"

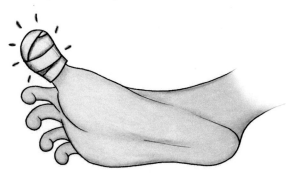

TOOTHBRUSH TED

I have a toothbrush, name of Ted,
A long thin body and a hairy head.
With a bright green jacket down to his waist,
He lives on a diet of mint toothpaste.
Shares it with me, as a good friend does.
When I press his button, he'll whirr and buzz.

He sits in his cup, morning and night,
His duty to make my teeth all white.
Holding the toothbrush very firm,
I squeeze the paste for a wiggly worm.
Round and round and back and fore,
Up and down and round once more.

And when my wobbly tooth fell out,
He said, "a grown-up tooth will sprout.
So when we brush, we'll mind the gap,
No need to get into a flap!"

I wrote a letter, "Dear Tooth Fairy,
When I smile, do I look scary?"
The Fairy answered, "Sleepy head,
I'll visit you when you're in bed."
And Ted buzzed from his toothbrush cup,
"You're very brave and all grown up."

Under the pillow in bed that night,
My tooth was hidden out of sight.
While cuddled up, all night I slept,
Her promise, the Tooth Fairy kept.

For fairies always tell the truth,
She left a coin and took my tooth!
Said Ted, "Just take your time, don't rush,
Cos we've got one less tooth to brush!"

Collecting teeth is quite a task,
"What happens to them all," I ask?

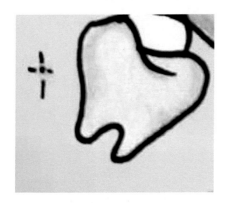

MY TOOTH

THE GREEDIES

Some folk are called the GREEDIES, you'll know them anywhere,
Because they're never satisfied and good behaviour's rare.
They can be very selfish, and push in front of you,
Especially at the ice-cream van, they often jump the queue.

Looks can be deceiving, this GREEDY 'sweet and young'
Responded when you smiled at her, by sticking out her tongue.
"I have no friends," she would complain, "it really isn't fair."
But who would want to play with her, she was too mean to share.

(You could check on Facebook, or other Social Media,
I guarantee you wouldn't find a person who was greedier!)

When Mum gave her an ice-cream, you could hear her roar,
"My ice-cream isn't big enough, d'you hear me, I want more."
Her Mummy said, "There is no more, you're never satisfied."
But as she was a GREEDY, she stamped her foot and cried.
She screamed and yelled out in a rage, a tantrum, what a scene,
"**I want, I want, I want, I want, I want;** you are so mean."

But meanwhile, feeling hungry, her little doggy Spot,
Crept unnoticed to her side and stole the blooming lot!
And so the moral of this tale, if there is someone needy,
You'll make more friends if you become a 'SHARER',
not a 'GREEDY'.

JUNGLE JIM'S GYM

Have you been to Jungle Jim's Gym,
At the local leisure centre?
It doesn't matter, fat or slim,
All animals can enter.

The Bear who wants to lose an ounce,
Hyenas who can't laugh,
The Kangaroo who's lost his bounce,
The wobbly neck Giraffe.

The Elephant who gave up chips,
(She wants to keep her figure),
She's lost some weight upon her hips,
But thinks her bum looks bigger.

The crotchety old Crocodile,
Looks younger than his years.
The treadmill's done it, walking miles,
Reduced the Croc to tears!

The Chimpanzee and Silverback,
Limber up with weights.
No time to slack, no time to snack,
And NO MORE piled-up plates!

Says Jim, "It's fun to to exercise,
We just don't do enough,
But those who do, are very wise,
No need to huff and puff!

Book a session, you'll get fit,
It's really a no-brainer."
Says Jungle Jim, "Just bring your kit,
I'll be your personal trainer."

ELLA-FANTASTIC

Ella was an elephant
Who hired an Ella-copter,
She'd go where others can or can't,
As long as no-one stopped her.

Said Ed and Fred her flying mates,
"It's gonna be a squeeze,
With both of us so overweight,
Let's hope that we don't sneeze!"

Ed said, "Today I packed my trunk,
It was a mammoth task.
I filled it up with lots of junk,
A sandwich and a flask."

Fred said, "Hooray, I've packed mine too,
I've no idea what's in it.
When we arrive the other end,
I probably will bin it."

The Copter Pilot doffed his cap
Said, "Stay clear of the door.
You can't sit on each other's lap,
Just one per seat, no more!"

All three of them the best of chums,
Each one enthusiastic,
Placed the seat-belts round their tums.
"Let's go, Ella-Fantastic."

The Pilot, Ella, Ed and Fred
Went whizzing through the sky
Although a hundred tons, who said,
'That elephants can't fly'?

THAT TAKES THE BISCUIT !

**Boom, bang, clatter, clang, clunk, clonk ,crash,
Slam, bam, bellow, boom, buzz, babble, bash.**

It's night-time in the kitchen, pots and pans are everywhere.

They fell out of the cupboard, and gave me such a scare.

I was looking for the biscuits; this isn't how I planned it,

And now big sister's on my tail, she's caught me out red-handed.

"You have dropped the cookie jar; it looks as if it's cracked,

Your hand is stuck right in it. I've caught you in the act!

You're going to be in trouble, when I tell Mum and Dad."

My sister's such a 'tell-tale', and they're gonna be so mad!

So much for my adventure; bye 'Biscuit Kid, the Hero'

And this week's pocket money, has gone right back to zero!

Worse, now I am the bad guy; I wish I hadn't risked it ,

And sister gets the credit! That REALLY *takes the biscuit.'*

LET'S DISCUSS.........

p4. ***CUSTARD ON TOAST***
If a relative offered you food that you didn't like, what would you say?

p6. ***SPELLBOUND***
Have you found the 'guilty' words? How many are there?

p7. ***GOOD IN-TENTS***
Have you been camping? Where did you go and in what did you sleep?

p8. ***ODD SOCKS***
What do 'coordinated colours' mean? How many socks are needed to make 6 matching pairs? What other clothes could you wear inside out, or back-to-front?

p10. ***PAWS FOR THOUGHT***
How many of you have pets? What are they? Who looks after them?

p11. ***MINDING THEIR OWN BUZZINESS***
What is nectar and where do bees find it?

p12. ***UP THE DOWNSTAIRS DOODAH***
Who are in charge in the land of Thingymajig and at what hour are they fast asleep? Can you draw a Goodle Watch?

p14. ***A SPIDER'S YARN***
Are you frightened of spiders? Why? How many legs does one spider and one fly have when added together?

p16. BYE BYE BUN

Does anyone have a pet rabbit? What is the name of Beatrix Potter's rabbit?

p17. MY OWN POEM

Who has written their own poem? Can you read it to us?

p19. PETE THE TWEET

Shall we repeat together the last line of each verse in a parrot's voice?

p20. WHAT AM I?

Have you done a drawing for this poem?

p21. STUFF

What 'stuff' do you collect and where do you store it?

p22. HOW LUCKY AM I?

In what way are the two friends the same, or different? In what ways can children be cruel to each other?

p23. WALLY WITH A BROLLY

What was not right? What does 'substitute' mean?

p24. BEST AT LAST

What is the 'moral' of this story? Why was Tim pleased with himself at the end of the race?

p28. PARTY ANIMALS

What animals do these names sound like? Jellyfant, Meringue-utang, Porkiepie, Flippopotoftea?

p30. A WIGGLE AND A GIGGLE

What is the 'moral' of this story. What does 'don't judge a bug just by its cover' mean?

p33. _MONKEY BUSINESS_
The Monkey and the Acorn are boasting. What do the words 'boasting' and 'respect' mean?

p33. _SHAKE RATTLE AND ROLL_
Can you think of other words not in this poem that have words inside them like 'sandwich' and 'ladder'?

p34. _A RUBBISH POEM_
What ideas do you have to save our planet?

p36. _A SPOT OF BOTHER_
Who has had chicken pox? Why it better to have it when you are young?

p38. _HEADS AND TOES_
Have you ever wanted to stay at home from school? Why?

p39. _TOOTHBRUSH TED_
Who has lost a tooth? What did you do with it? What do you think the fairies do with the teeth they collect?

p43. _THE GREEDIES_
What does being greedy mean?

p44. _JUNGLE JIM 'S GYM_
Do you exercise? Which ones do you do?

p46. _ELLA- FANTASTIC_
What is the difference between an aeroplane and a helicopter?

p48. _THAT TAKES THE BISCUIT_
What does this title mean? Was his sister right to tell their Mum and Dad?

MY BOOK ENDS

CUSTARD ON TOAST, that's my name,
For you to read me, was my aim.
Did you write your poem too,
On the page designed for you?

And if you thought you would be bored,
That poetry should be ignored.
Like broccoli, I should be tried,
A taste of verse, and then decide!

Page 20 asked you 'What Am I ?
A pie, a spy, a fly, an eye ?'
Imagine your unique creation,
Then draw your own interpretation.

Have you enjoyed my poetry?
It can be fun, do you agree?
And if you liked me, tell your friends,
Till then, this is where **MY BOOK ENDS!**